OF MESS *and* MOXIE JOURNAL

JEN HATMAKER

An Imprint of Thomas Nelson

Published in Nashville, Tennessee, by Nelson Books, an imprint of Thomas Nelson. Nelson Books and Thomas Nelson are registered trademarks of HarperCollins Christian Publishing, Inc.

Published in association with Yates & Yates, www.yates2.com.

Thomas Nelson titles may be purchased in bulk for educational, business, fund-raising, or sales promotional use. For information, please e-mail SpecialMarkets@ThomasNelson.com.

ISBN 978-1-4041-0632-1

Printed in China

17 18 19 20 21 DSC 10 9 8 7 6 5 4 3 2 1

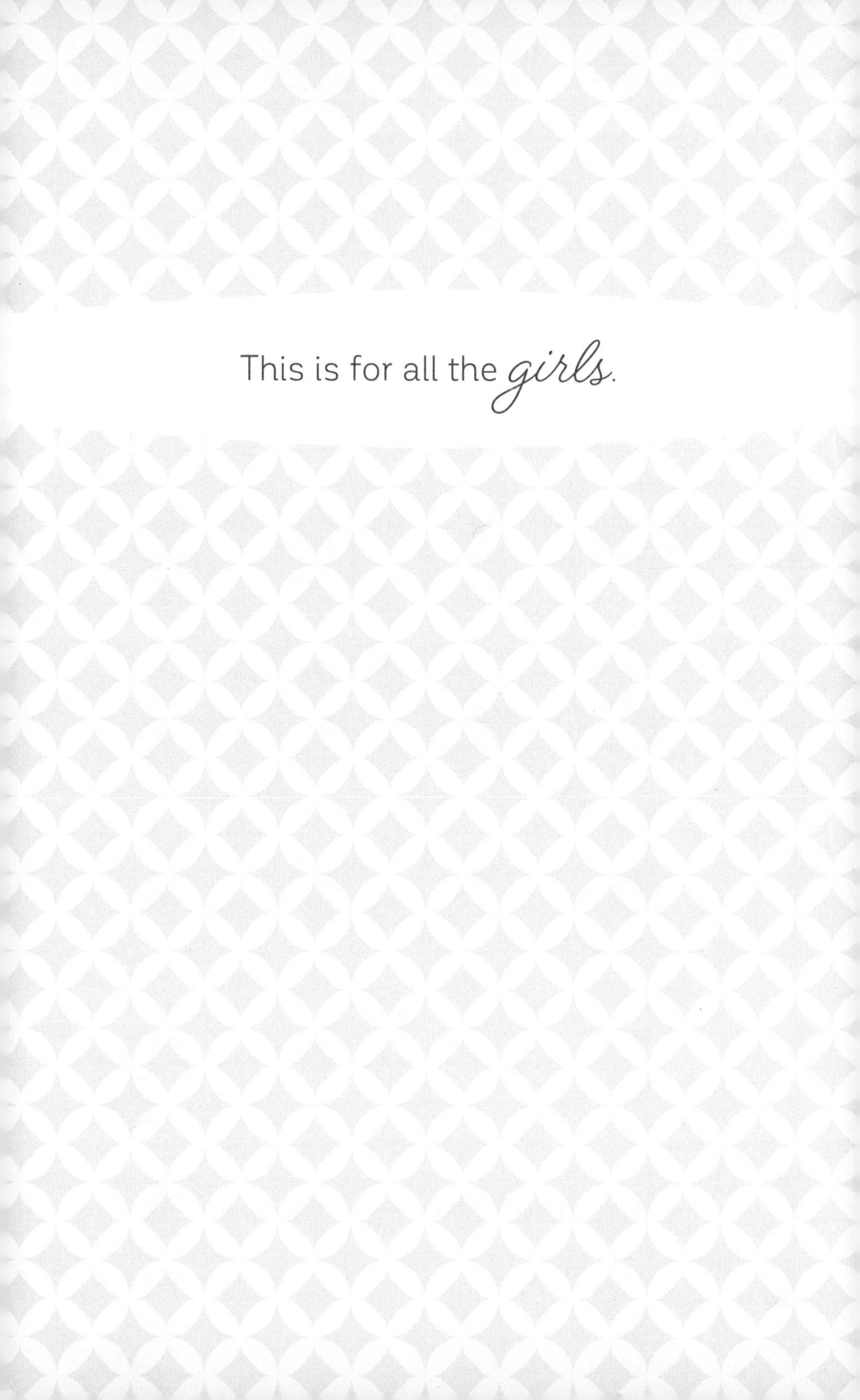

This is for all the *girls*.

M*oxie*. Isn't that a delicious, dreamy word? Moxie. It is a throwback to women with pluck, with chutzpah, with a bit of razzle dazzle.

It says: I got this . . . . we got this *together*.

We are spread out across geography, generations, and experiences, but we have two important things in common: mess and moxie.

Moxie reaches for laughter, for courage, for the deep and important truth that women are capable of weathering the storm.

We are not *victims*, we are not *weak*, we are not a sad, defeated group of sob sisters.

Yes, life is hard, but we are incredibly resilient. It is how God created us!

He said, "Let there be *moxie*!" and it was *good* (paraphrased).

I've let the fridge and pantry whittle down to half a package of rice and an old bottle of fish sauce before finally dragging my butt to the store to fend off starvation. Why is it so hard? Wasn't I just here?

Are malnourished *robbers* breaking in at night and eating our food?

Rather than waiting for the Someday life or, conversely, imagining our Someday life is in the rearview mirror and we'll never reclaim it, what if we embraced it all right now?

All the *hope*, all the thrill, all the *growth*, all the possibility?

Sometimes my mess outpaces my moxie, and no one has the good sense to deactivate my social media accounts so I will not become an actual threat to the kingdom of God.

You are far more than your worst day, your worst experience, your worst season, dear one. You are more than the sorriest decision you ever made. You are more than the darkest sorrow you've endured.

Your name is *not* Ruined. It is *not* Helpless.
It is *not* Victim. It is *not* Irresponsible.

God created us to triumph; we are made in the image of Jesus, who has overcome the world. We are never defeated, not even when all evidence appears to the contrary.

If you are still breathing, there is always tomorrow, and it can always be new.

This is for all you girls about twenty-three. You're here, bursting into adulthood.

We who are ahead of you are so *glad* you made it!

You might not necessarily be *leaving* one thing but *running toward* something else.

This is the price of being a human being on this planet; we get the glorious and the grueling, and surprisingly, the second often leads to the first. Trust this messy transparent who loves you.

We are in the same boat.

Forgiveness does not erase your past—a healed memory is not a deleted memory—but it does enlarge your future, increase your love, and set you free.

How to lose baby weight: Tell yourself you can do it. Look how great you were at *gaining* the weight!

Positive *affirmation* is important here.

The whole idea of planning out two weeks of meals and recipes and lists makes me want to cover my eyes like a southern damsel.

I mean, *I write entire books* but can't *muster* the discipline to compile a one-page list.

It is simply understood that game day recipes can involve a disproportionate amount of mayonnaise, cheese, red meat, or TTAF (things that are fried).

TTAF!

God gives us both Good News and good times, and neither cancels out the other.

What a wonderful world, what a wonderful life, what a *wonderful* God.

When we sow seeds of love into our children, between our children, it will eventually bear fruit. Our job is just to plant, plant, plant, and wait.

Love makes us brave, pulls up seats to the table, defuses bigotry, and attacks injustice. It is our most powerful spiritual tool. Do not underestimate it as the solution to almost everything that is broken.

Women have the innate capacity to nurture their own art without a paycheck, audience, outside permission, or charitable intentions.

This is for all you girls around thirty-eight. . . . You have some really beautiful dreams; some of them are already realized, some are half-baked, some live privately in your secret stash of yearnings. . . . You won't find a bigger fan than me.

I am convinced there is nothing we cannot tackle, solve, endure, or dream. You're smart. Your work is meaningful, and it is mattering. I am proud of you, proud to belong to you. I *believe* in us.

I believe we can take a handful of things quite seriously as parents and take the rest less seriously, and it is all going to be okay. You are doing an amazing job.

The truth is, God created us with resiliency. Mankind is incredibly able to heal, to rise back up, to stare down pain with moxie. Jesus strengthens our minds for the task of recovery.

We've got *chops*, girls.

How to go swimsuit shopping three months postpartum: Gather as many "figure-flattering" swimsuits as possible. Hastily try them on. Look in the mirror, but only through squinted eyes to soften the blow.

Wear *sunglasses* if this helps.

We live because Jesus lives, because He is real and present and moving and working and He will not have us conquered.

I cannot write a good story if I am not living one.

How could we imagine that a God who created wildflowers and waterfalls and pine trees and hummingbirds and warm sand and mountain ranges and tulips thinks beauty is nonsense?

You can love someone the church condemns. You have no other responsibility than to represent Jesus well, which should leave that person feeling absurdly loved, welcomed, cherished. There is no other end game.

You are not anyone's savior; you are a sister.

How to ensure people feel compelled to pop in for a visit . . .

Place someone's underwear in an obscure but *visible* area.

I sincerely believe we are created by a Creator to be creative. This is part of His image we bear, this bringing forth of beauty, life, newness.

God never coddles me when I want Him to.

It's *infuriating.*

Cooking dinner is a sacred gateway from work to rest, from seven separate lives to one shared table.

You don't have to be who you were.

What is not to love about a guy who pulled children onto His lap and saved a failing party and touched the untouchables and told off the religious elite?

How to grow an insanely long chin or neck hair when you're thirty-seven . . .

Blink. That should do it.

I possess full confidence in God but a healthy skepticism of the human understanding of God.

Loving your teens means loving their friends, and the formula is easy: feed them constantly and ask good questions about their lives. The end.

Making your home pretty is nice, but making it nourishing is holy.

Love means saying to someone else's story or pain or anger or experience: "I'm listening. Tell me more."

This is for all you girls about fifty-nine. You've done it!

You raised the kids, survived the crowded years, and five-plus decades of life look so *good* on you.

A life spent entirely on pleasure is the emptiest of containers. We know this in our souls, in our Scriptures. God positively told us to stay close to the brokenhearted, the hungry, the hurting . . .

. . . that is where He is and where some of His *best* work is going down.

No strings. You can love truly, without conditions, without agenda, without a fork in the road, without disapproval, without fear, without obligation.

Gather round, young ones, and I will tell you a tale that will frighten and confuse you. . . . Once upon a time, there was no such thing as Netflix.

We had what was called "basic cable," which meant that shows aired on four channels on a certain day at a certain time. And that is the *end* of the *tale*.

There is nothing weak about being in the care of a counselor. That is strong, sister.

The longer we keep our heartaches tucked away in the dark, the more menacing they become. Pulling them into the light among trusted people who love you is, I swear, 50 percent of the recovery process.

How to have the sex talk with your elementary-age kid: when asked where babies come from, first say God.

When pressed, say *Jesus.*

Rather than fantasizing about greener grass on some other side, *water your own grass first*, because there is no marriage, no union that doesn't have its share of aggravations and struggles.

If you feel stuck today, can I suggest approaching the doldrums in a reasonable way, one tiny element at a time? Alone, none are monumental, but together they lay small paver stones out of the mire, forging a path back to health, back to vibrancy.

Why even have a porch if there is no TV on it for playoffs?

We're not *amateurs.*

The thing is, God absolutely created us and His world with tastes and sights and sounds and connections designed to thrill. He thought up humor and laughter and delicious flavors coaxed from the earth.

He gave us *beautiful* colors and dance and music and the gift of language. He invented apples and beaches and sex and baby lambs.

Family is far more resilient than I ever hoped.

The way we treat others should lead them to only one conclusion: "If this is how Jesus loves, then I'm in."

When in doubt, ask yourself: What would *love* feel like here, to this person?

Simply identifying fear as the dominant emotion is a helpful red flag. It tells us: Whoa up, sister. These thoughts and ideas cannot be trusted.

The entire story of God reveals a vast, encompassing campaign to love humanity all the way home.

That thing in you that wants to make something beautiful?

It is *holy.*

Marriage is not designed to make you forfeit your soul.

Loved people love people. Forgiven people forgive people.

Adored people *adore* people.
Freed people *free* people.

If we get seven out of ten things mostly right as moms, we are winning the majority, and the majority wins the race.

If we absorb the full counsel of Scripture and acknowledge that God sincerely loves us and gave us a whole world of gifts and joys, we discover many secular things we love are actually sacred.

How to find a family pet: visit the local shelter's Open House.

Overestimate your willpower.

Never fear, Mamas, the energy you are logging toward any tradition will not return void.

You are building something *special*, and your kids will not forget.

Worry less about getting recognized and more about becoming good at what you do. Take yourself seriously. Take your art seriously. You are both worth this.

There is only Jesus and His band of scalawags and ragamuffins. Find your people. They exist.

Raise your *voice*, tell your *story*,
take your *place*.

No one can wound us more than those supposed to nurture: our parents, our spouses, our churches. The chasm between expectation and reality is particularly grim in supposed safe places.

The aging, uncooperative body is one thing, but the gym is a whole 'nother situation. It becomes immediately clear that many people there have been using the membership they paid for.

What is this, the Try Hard Convention?
Where my *sloths* at?

Forgiveness is not condoning evil, not forgetting, not brushing something under the carpet, not a free pass. It does not mean minimizing the injury and, consequently, your pain.

Our teens need to know that we are *for them* and *with them*, not just when they are performing well but in struggle, failure, calamity. This is, after all, exactly how God loves us.

People may hate us because of Jesus, but they should never hate Jesus because of us.

I'll approach a weight machine absolutely flummoxed on how to use it. So instead of asking for help like a mature adult, I loosely figure out where the butt, hands, and legs go and just push, pull, squeeze, lift accordingly.

Sometimes I am facing the
entirely *wrong* direction.

You offer depth and nuance and perception to every conversation we share, and the tribe is immeasurably better for it.

We have only a few days on earth in the scope of history. We get one shot at this, one chance to live in a way that brings true honor to God, the great Lover of people.

There is no scarcity in creativity. The world always needs good offerings. We cannot have too much beauty. There is no such thing as too much wisdom and literature and story and craftsmanship.

How to guarantee the dog will throw up on your bed—Option 1: Get a brand-new quilt, comforter, or duvet.

Option 2: Wash the current one.

We are smart and resilient and so very funny and capable, and the days ahead of us stretch unwritten, unsullied, untarnished: still standing. That's our moxie.

We have *everything* we need.

Every time I read how Jesus described the kingdom as a seed or yeast, I think of parenthood. That seed is planted, that yeast is mixed in, but, my gosh, you cannot see anything happening for a while.

Art is worth every second. So here I am, creators, cheering you on. We need you. We need your stories and craftsmanship and gifts and courage.

....

....

....

....

....

....

....

....

....

....

....

....

....

....

....

Here we all are: still standing. Still standing. We have breath in our lungs: still standing. We have people who love us: still standing. We have a God who spends all His hours making broken things whole again.

Still *standing.*

This for all the girls. The ones who thought they'd be married by now but are still single, who thought they'd be mothers by now but aren't, who said they didn't want children and have four. The ones whose marriages didn't work, the ones who found love a second time.